℞ RAVETTE BOOKS

Copyright © 1987 United Feature Syndicate, Inc.
All Rights Reserved. Originally Published by
Australian Consolidated Press.

First reprint by Ravette Books Limited 1989
Second reprint 1990

This book is sold subject to the condition that it shall not,
by way of trade or otherwise, be lent, re-sold, hired out or
otherwise circulated without the publisher's prior consent
in any form of binding or cover other than that in which
this is published and without a similar condition including
this condition being imposed on the subsequent
purchaser.

Printed and bound for Ravette Books Limited,
3 Glenside Estate, Star Road,
Partridge Green, Nr. Horsham,
West Sussex RH13 8RA
by Mateu Cromo Artes Gráfica, s.a.

ISBN: 1 85304 107 6

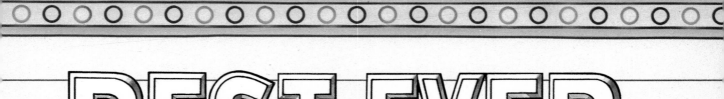

BEST EVER

ADAPTATION TO A
"Hospital Environment"

BEST EVER

ACHIEVEMENT BY A
CAT IN A **"Wet Medium"**

I FEEL INVINCIBLE TODAY

FOOD! I CRAVE FOOD!

THAT TOOK NEARLY THREE SECONDS, JON. WE'LL DO BETTER NEXT TIME, WON'T WE?

I SHALL TAKE MY MORNING STROLL NOW. BE A GOOD BOY AND ALERT THE MEDIA

HOLD UP, TRAFFIC. HERE COMES GARFIELD

WHERE WERE YOU?

LEARNING THAT SOME THINGS CAN'T BE INTIMIDATED

JIM DAVIS

4-15

BEST EVER

BEST EVER

IMITATION OF A
"Surprise Package"

BEST EVER

ENDURANCE IN A
"TV Movie Marathon"

GOOD EVENING, FOLKS. HERE'S A JOKE... WHAT DID THE BEAVER SAY WHEN HE HEARD THE CHAIN SAW?

CHUKONG!

CHIRP

CHIRP

THEY'RE PLAYING MY SONG

ALL OF YOUR MOTHERS WEAR ARMY BOOTS

JIM DAVIS

KONK

CRASH!

BAP!

-20

WHY DO YOU DO IT, GARFIELD?

I LOOOOVE THE ATTENTION

RRRRRR

JON'S BEST SHOES!

SOMETIMES ODIE MAKES ME SO ANGRY, I COULD JUST SCREAM

ARRRRRGH!

JIM DAVIS

6-3

BEST EVER

SKATEBOARDING IN A
"'Down Hill Event"

YAWN

IT'S BEDDY-BYE TIME AGAIN

TONIGHT I THINK I'LL TAKE A DEEP BREATH, SLOWLY CLOSE MY EYES AND SAVOR THE HEAVY FEELING OF SLEEP GRADUALLY OVERTAKING MY BODY

PAT!

PAT!

PAT!

THEN AGAIN IT WOULD BE FUN TO HAVE A CUP OF COFFEE AND TOSS AND TURN FOR A COUPLE OF HOURS, THEN SLEEP 'TIL NOON

OR MAYBE I'LL RUN AROUND THE BLOCK, COLLAPSE INTO BED EXHAUSTED AND FALL ASLEEP INSTANTLY

OR I COULD WATCH THE ALL-NIGHT MOVIES ON TV UNTIL MY EYELIDS GET SO HEAVY I COULDN'T POSSIBLY HOLD THEM OPEN ANY LONGER

SIGH ... SO MUCH SLEEPING TO DO AND SO FEW NIGHTS

JIM DAVIS

6-24

I BELIEVE YOU'RE GAINING WEIGHT, GARFIELD

I BELIEVE YOUR EYEBALLS ARE SHRINKING

LOOK AT THAT SOFT BELLY

THAT'S JUST WATER RETENTION

© 1984 United Feature Syndicate, Inc.

NOW WHY DO YOU SUPPOSE YOU'RE LOOKING LARGER?

AN OPTICAL ILLUSION?

JIM DAVIS

THE OLDER YOU GET, THE BIGGER YOU GET

BIGGER-BONED MAYBE

YOU'RE FAT, GARFIELD

I AM NOT FAT!

7-1

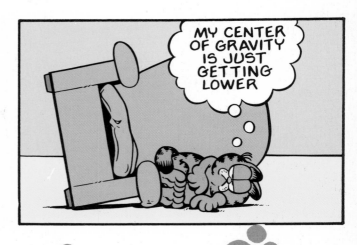

MY CENTER OF GRAVITY IS JUST GETTING LOWER

I'LL BE DARNED. THESE LABELS ARE LOOSE

IT'S THE OLD "CAT GETS THE TUNA WHILE THE OWNER GETS THE CAT FOOD" GAG

© 1984 United Feature Syndicate, Inc.

SURPRISE, GARFIELD! I FIXED US A TUNA NOODLE CASSEROLE

OH, WELL, I GUESS A HALF A SURPRISE IS BETTER THAN NONE AT ALL

7-8

JIM DAVIS

BEST EVER

PERFORMANCE OF AN
"Unhappy Pen-Pal"

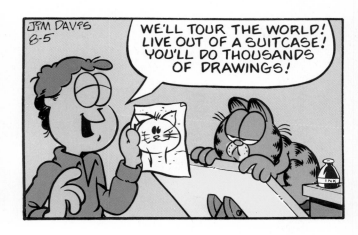

THIS LADDER GIVES ME A GREAT IDEA

I'M GOING TO GLUE MY FEET TO THE CEILING

AND BLOW JON'S MIND

THIS IS GOING TO BE FUN

UNLESS, OF COURSE, JON DOESN'T SEE ME

© 1984 United Feature Syndicate, Inc.

UNLESS, OF COURSE, JON GOES TO BED

JIM DAVIS 8-26

BEST EVER

HERE WE ARE, BOYS. WE'RE CAMPING MILES FROM NOWHERE

I'D SAY WE'RE CLOSER THAN THAT

CLICK

OH NO! ODIE'S LOCKED HIMSELF IN THE CAR! THE POOR LITTLE GUY COULD SUFFOCATE!

I THINK I'M STARTING TO ENJOY CAMPING

UNLOCK THE DOOR, BOY. UNLOCK THE DOOR

BREATHE DEEPLY, BOY

JIM DAVIS 9-2

SOMETHING JUST OCCURRED TO ME. COULD IT BE...?

COULD IT BE, ODIE ISN'T AS STUPID AS HE LOOKS?

CHIPS

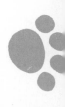

BEST EVER

WHY, HELLO, NERMAL. AREN'T YOU CUTE

I WANT SOME ATTENTION, TOO

BONK

AW, POOR LITTLE GUY!

WELL, TWO CAN PLAY THE SYMPATHY GAME

CRASH!

JIM DAVIS 9-9   © 1984 United Feature Syndicate, Inc.

THAT WAS ONE OF MY BEST PLATES

THAT WAS ONE OF MY BEST HEADS

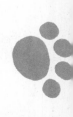